Right@Sight
Grade 2

Based on
Read and Play
(original and new series) by
T. A. Johnson

Revised by Caroline Evans

With additional material by Paul Terry

London · Frankfurt · Leipzig · New York

Peters Edition Limited
10–12 Baches Street
London
N1 6DN

First published 2001
© 2001 by Hinrichsen Edition, Peters Edition Limited, London

Music-setting and typesetting by Musonix

Cover design by Nick Wakelin and Adam Hay
Text design by c eye, London
Printed in Great Britain by Caligraving Limited
Thetford, Norfolk

Set in Monotype Garamond 3 and Frutiger

Right@Sight

Grade 2

A note to teachers

Sight-reading is one of the most important skills for any musician, and certainly not to be seen as a chore necessary only for passing exams! Right@Sight will help to develop and improve that skill, providing a structured approach and opportunities for regular practice. Hints are provided for the earlier pieces to focus attention on notation, form, interpretation and technique, prompted with questions (left-hand column) and information (right). Suggestions to sight-sing phrases are included to promote aural awareness while playing.

In an examination, half a minute will be given to prepare the sight-reading, and the examiner is likely to remind candidates that they may play the music during this time. Encourage your students to try out the opening, the ending and any awkward-looking passages so that they are well prepared before the test starts. Instil careful attention to the fundamental elements of Time, Rhythm and Key – though the key signature comes first on the staff, it is often the first piece of information to be forgotten in performance!

Becoming a good sight-reader needs daily practice, and regular 'exercise' with Right@Sight will prepare students to tackle whatever music they may want to play. Towards the end of the section with commentary, some pieces go a little beyond the standard expected for the grade, so as to stretch players' ability and enable them to face any sight-reading test with increased confidence: to play it right – at sight!

Caroline Evans

Key to symbols

1	Exercise number
T	Time
R	Rhythm
K	Key
?	Questions
!	Watch out

Contents

Hands together in the keys of C, G, D and F major; A and D minor

1 Follow the **TRaK**

| **T** | What is the time signature? | The value of each beat is a crotchet. |

R Can you tap the rhythm: right hand on the right knee and left hand on the left knee?

Count while tapping.

K What is the key?

Play the tonic (key-note).

? How should you play the slurred notes?

In contrast, keep the *staccato* notes in bars 3 to 7 gently detached.

Can you study the fingering?

In bar 5 there is a closing in (contraction) of the thumb to E and an opening out (extension) of the 5th finger in order to reach the C.

Relax when you play this but try not to hesitate. Look ahead.

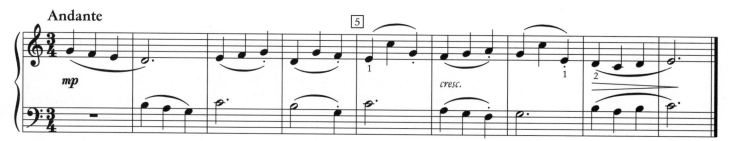

2 **TRaK**

Check the time signature; tap the rhythm; and find the key.

? How many beats in the final right-hand note?

Make sure both hands finish together in the last bar.

Does the left hand have to change position?

Use the rest in bar 4 to move the position of the right hand up by one note.

! **Watch out** for the extension of the right thumb in bar 6.

Have your right hand in position before you begin.
Imagine military drums playing the left hand part at the start.

Follow the TRaK

? How many beats are there in a dotted minim?

Find all the notes to be sharpened.
Play and name the broken chord in bar 5 (right hand).

Be sure to hold the tied notes for their full value.

Notice the closing in (contraction) of the thumb and 3rd finger in bars 5 to 6 (right hand).

! **Watch out** for the slight change of hand position at bar 4 (right hand).

Play smoothly (*legato*) not forgetting the *ritenuto* in the final bars.
Remember both sharps in the key signature.

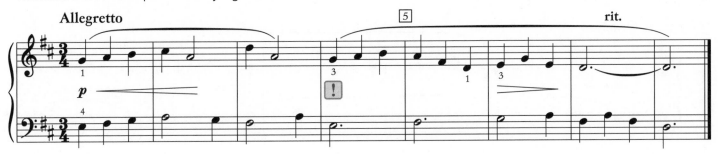

TRaK

R On which beat does the right hand begin?

K What is the key?

? Which is the best finger to use for the F♯s in bar 6 (right hand)?

Remember to count as you tap the rhythm.

Find all the F♯s in the piece.

Note the fingerings in bar 4.

! **Watch out** for the ledger line notes in the left hand (middle C and D).

Use the crotchet rests in bar 5 to find the first notes in bar 6.
Play very firmly, making the *forte* loud but not harsh in tone.

5

[T] How many beats are there in a bar?

[R] Can you tap the rhythm?

[K] What does the key signature tell you?

[?] Do you notice the rising pattern of the melody in the first four bars?

In which bar does the thumb have to pass under the fingers (right hand)?

The value of the beat is a crotchet.

Hold all dotted minims for their full value.

Play the tonic (key-note). Find all the B♭s.

The melody is shared by both hands, passing from the left hand to the right in bars 1–2 and in bars 5–6.

Note the change of hand position in bar 6 (right hand).

Play gracefully and smoothly (*legato*).

6

[TRaK]

[?] Can you observe the rests in bars 2, 3, 4 and 6?

Can you plan the fingering?

Find all the B♭s.

Make sure that the C in bar 2 (left hand) enters on beat 2 after the crotchet rest.

The 2nd finger passes over the thumb in bar 4 (right hand).

Play steadily with a good firm tone.

TRaK

[?] What is a minuet?

Which is the best finger to use for the first note in the right hand?

[!] **Watch out** for the ledger line note, D above middle C, in bar 2 (left hand).

Find all the F♯s.

This should be played at a moderate pace.

Notice that the 2nd finger passes over the thumb in the right hand of bar 4.

Play fairly quietly and gracefully.

TRaK

[?] Can you tap the rhythm accurately first time?

Is the key major or minor?

[!] **Watch out** for the quavers in contrary motion in bar 6.

Count as you tap so that the timing of all the rests is correct.

Find the B♭s. Decide whether the last two notes in the left hand of bar 4 should be sharps, flats or naturals.

Play very lightly.

9 **TRaK**

R On which beat does the melody begin?

? What do you notice about the melody in the opening bars?

Can you observe all the slurs and *staccato* notes?

! **Watch out** for the accidental in bar 5 (right hand).

Count carefully, especially in bars 3, 4 and 7.

Count aloud two beats before you play.

Notice how the left hand seems to mirror the right hand melody at the beginning.

Lift your wrist a little after each slurred group.

Be prepared: place your left hand over the notes **before** you begin the piece with the right hand.

10 **T** How many beats are there in a bar?

R Can you count as you tap the rhythm with both hands?

K Is the key major or minor?

? Can you look at the fingering, especially the closing in of the 4th finger in bar 7 (right hand)?

What does *rit.* tell you to do in bar 7?

Give the value of the beat.

See that the quavers in both hands are correctly timed.

Look at bars 7 and 8 to help you decide on the key.

Find all the ledger line notes in the left hand.

8

Follow the TRaK

Look at the time signature; tap the rhythm; name the key. Find the B♭s.

? Can you study the fingering?

Note the contraction (closing in) of the 5th finger in the right hand in bar 7.

What does *cresc.* mean?

Bar 5 must be very much quieter than bars 1–4.

Try humming the first four bars in the right hand **before** you play the piece. Try again afterwards.

TRaK

R What is the value of the dotted crotchet in bar 2 (left hand)?

Count carefully here when you tap the rhythm. Also count the minims precisely.

K Is the key major or minor?

Look for an accidental.

? Can you follow the dynamics?

Bars 5–6 should sound like a distant echo of bars 3–4.

! **Watch out** for the rest in bar 8 (left hand).

Play firmly and steadily. Make the contrast in dynamics really distinct, with a *fortissimo* in the final bars. Look ahead.

13

Follow the [TRaK]

[?] What do you notice about the opening figure in the right hand and that in the left hand?

What do the dots above and below many of the notes mean?

[!] **Watch out** for the chromatic note in bar 7.

Find the broken chords.

Take care to time all the rests and quaver groups correctly.

Aim for a real contrast between the staccato notes and those that should be held for their full length.

14

[TRaK]

[K] How often does F♯ occur?

[?] Can you find some broken chords and scale patterns?

Can you follow the fingering?

[!] **Watch out** for the rests on the fourth beat of bar 4.

Tap and count.

Play the tonic chord.

Compare bars 1 and 2 with bars 5 and 6.

In bars 1 and 5 (RH), the 2nd finger turns over the thumb. In bar 4 the thumb goes under the 3rd finger.

Play steadily and very *legato*. Make sure that the final chords are played exactly together.

T

R

K

? What do you notice about the melody in bars 1 to 3 and in bars 5 to 6 (RH)?

Can you study the fingering in bar 5 where the thumb turns under the 2nd finger (RH)?

This is simple triple time.

Count carefully when you tap the ♩. ♪ rhythm.

Find all the notes to be flattened.

When a melody or a harmonic pattern is repeated immediately at another pitch, it is called a sequence.

The left hand remains in the five finger position all the way through.

Try and hum the tune in your head before you play. Play very smoothly and note the *crescendo* towards the end.

 TRaK

? Do you notice the scale passages in imitation, and the brief contrary motion?

Remember both sharps in the key signature.

Compare both phrases.

Try humming the melody in the right hand before you begin. Play firmly.
Play through the piece again two bars at a time and hum the melody as an echo.

17

Look at the TRaK

[R] Can you tap the rhythm, timing all the rests correctly?

[?] Can you find any passages where the melody is repeated at a different pitch?

Can you make a note of the change of finger on C in bar 8 (LH)?

Common time **𝄴** means that there are ......

.... beats in a bar.

Give the tied notes in the left hand their full value.

This is called a ....
(See No. 15 for the answer).

Note the change of hand position in bars 3 and 5 (RH), also in bars 3, 5 and 9 (LH).

Play without stopping, observing all the dynamics. Note the little coda.

18

Follow the TRaK

[K] Is the key major or minor?

[?] Where is a broken chord of D minor used?

What is the meaning of *Andante*?

[!] **Watch out** for the accented quaver in bar 6, followed by a quaver rest; and also the dotted crotchet in bar 7.

Note the accidental in bar 4 (RH). Play the tonic note.

Give the meaning of *rit. e dim.*

TRaK

R Can you tap the rhythm several times first?

? Which hand has the melody in bars 4 to 8?

What is the meaning of *ben marcato*?

Play the broken chords in bars 5, 6 and 7 as block chords.

Count as you tap, making sure that the quavers in bar 3 (LH), and in bars 5–8 (RH) enter at the correct time.

Try to make the contrasts in dynamics really distinct.

Contrast the accented notes with the light and crisp *staccato* notes in the second phrase.

Play rhythmically.

TRaK

? Can you find any scale patterns?

What are the intervals in the right-hand chords in bars 5, 6, 7 and 8?

Play the tonic chord. Find the B♭s.

Notice the little contrary motion in bars 3 to 4.

Try and place your fingers over the chords just **before** you have to play them.

Always look ahead, and be prepared for the changes of hand position. Observe the dynamics.

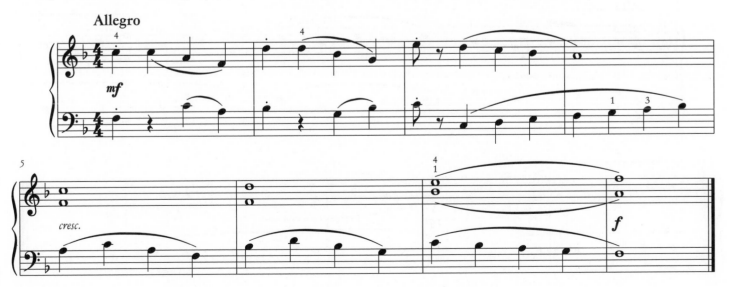

Follow the **TRaK**

 What is a minuet?

How should you change tempo in bar 7?

Can you spot the descending scale passage in bar 5?

Can you look at the fingering carefully?

Find all the notes to be raised one semitone.

Decide on a suitable speed (tempo) for this piece.

Notice that you also change the dynamics in bar 7.

Play the quavers evenly, taking care with the slurs and *staccato* notes.

Note the changes of hand position.

Play in an elegant and stately manner.

TRaK

 What do you notice about the pattern of the notes in both hands for the first six bars?

Are there any tied notes?

Can you study the fingering?

Is there a change of hand position?

Find all the B♭s and any accidentals.

Note the coda (the extra two bars added to the end of the piece).

Count carefully in the last few bars.

Note the contraction necessary between the 2nd finger and the 5th finger in bars 6 and 7 (RH).

Look at bar 9 (RH). The left hand remains in the five finger position throughout.

! **Watch out** – bar 6 is quite tricky. Play this on its own first.

This march is in contrasting style to No. 21. Play the whole piece through very rhythmically.

T How many beats are there in a bar?	
R What is the meaning of **ritmico**?	Tap this **tango** rhythm several times, with hands separately and together.
K Can you name the key?	Find all the F#s and any accidentals.
? What do you notice when you compare the right-hand melody with that in the left hand?	Notice how the left hand imitates the right hand in the first few bars.
Can you make a note of the changes of hand position in bars 3, 5 and 7 (RH), and bar 4 (LH)?	In order to make the repeated notes sound clearer and more rhythmic, it is a good idea to change fingers here.

A tango is a dance, said to have originated in Africa, which later became established in Argentina.
Contrast the *staccato* notes in bars 5 to 6 with the accented minims which follow.

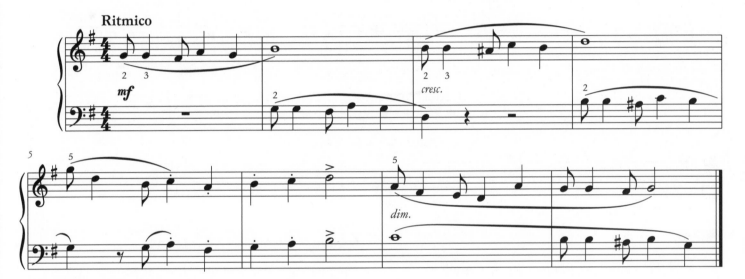

TRaK

K Is the key major or minor?	Look at the G# accidentals to help you name the key.
Is the chord in the last two bars major or minor?	When a major third in the tonic chord concludes a piece in the minor key it is called a *tierce de Picardie*.
? Are there any tied notes?	Make sure that the tied notes are held for their full value while you are playing the left-hand notes.
Can you study the fingering?	There are two extensions of the hand position in bars 2 to 3, and bar 4 (RH), and a contraction from E in bar 3 to A in bar 4 (RH).

Count carefully especially with the right-hand entry in bar 1. Play very quietly and sadly.

25 TRaK

This piece has a similar rhythm to No. 23.
Tap several times first.

Find all the accidentals.

[?] Can you find any small scale passages?   Note the broken chord in bar 4.

Can you look at the fingering especially in bar 6 (RH)?   Find all the changes of hand position.

Keep looking ahead and keep counting. Play this with force and energy.

26 TRaK

Place the correct finger on the accidentals.

[?] Can you spot the imitation in bars 1 and 2?

The melody is transferred to the left hand in bars 5 and 6, then returns to the right hand.

Can you study the fingering?

Note the contraction in bar 3 (RH) between the 5th and 2nd fingers in order to reach the A in bar 4. There is also a change of hand position in bar 7 (LH).

Do not forget the accent in bar 2 (RH), and observe the *staccato* notes. Play this fairly quickly.

Follow the **TRaK**

[?] Which parts are to be played *staccato* and which are to be played *legato*?

Can you study the fingering?

Tap the rhythm, both parts together.

Make these differences in articulation really clear.

In bar 3 (LH) the thumb turns under the 2nd finger. Also in bar 3 (RH), the 3rd finger turns over the thumb which has played the A in the previous bar.

Remember to hold the final chord for its full value.

Play in a lively manner.

TRaK

[?] What do you notice about the fingering on the repeated notes in the first six bars?

Do you know what *Alla marcia* means?

[!] Watch out in bars 4–5 (RH). The D is accented and then tied in bar 5.

Observe all the crotchet rests.

There is only one black note in the whole piece – don't forget where it is!

The style of this piece relies on a neat performance of *staccato* notes and slurs in the first six bars.
Play with a good firm tone observing the *fortissimo* in bar 4 and the *diminuendo* at the end.

TRaK

? What is the interval between the two notes in the left hand in bars 1 to 4?

Remember the two sharps in D major.

Notice the climbing melodic interval of a fourth in bars 2, 3 and 4 (RH). Notice also how the harmonic intervals in bars 7, 8 and 9 (LH) grow progressively larger as they descend.

At first you might find it tricky to play *legato* in one hand while the other is playing *staccato*.
First, play the piece slowly to practise this technique. Play it again in a more lively fashion.

30

T This is simple triple time.

R Tap the rhythm.

K Name the key. Play the broken chords.

? Do you notice the echo effect in bars 3 and 4; and also the descending pattern of the melody?

The melody is shared by both hands.

Can you look at the fingering, especially bars 10–11?

Find any changes of hand position.

Try to observe the dynamics, and also the phrasing. Keep counting in your head as you play this through gracefully.

TRaK

T What is the value of the beat?

R How many tied notes are there?

? Is there any imitation between the hands?

Are there any changes of hand position?

Another name for $\frac{2}{2}$ time is ....

Make sure that the tied notes are all held for the correct number of beats.

Be prepared for the changes in hand position when the melody passes from one hand to the other.

Do not begin too quietly otherwise a *pianissimo* at the end will not be achieved effectively. Try using the sustaining pedal in the final bars. Play through steadily. Then play the right hand again, four bars at a time, and sing as an echo.

TRaK

? Do you notice the slurred couplets in bars 7, 8 and 9 (RH)?

Can you make a note of the change of fingers on the Ds in bar 5 (RH)?

Remember both the sharps in the key signature.

Play the slurs neatly: drop the wrist on the first note, then lift the wrist slightly on the second note.

Look for any slight extensions or contractions, or changes in hand position.

Contrast the slurs with crisp and light *staccato* playing.

33 Follow the TRaK

K   Is the key major or minor?

Look at the accidentals and the tonic, or key-note, before deciding on the key.

?   What do you notice about the melody in bars 1 and 2 compared with that in bars 5 and 6?

Note how the left-hand melody in bars 5 and 6 moves into the treble clef as the right hand takes it over.

As this piece moves mainly by step it should not be too difficult to imagine what it sounds like before playing it. Play slowly and in a stately manner (*Largo*).

34 TRaK

The C♯ in bar 7 (LH) suggests a key change. Try and name it.

?   Do you notice all the little scale patterns in the right hand?

Try to observe the slurred couplets and *staccato* notes.

Can you study the fingering, even in the coda?

Note any changes of hand position, especially in bar 11.

Play lightly (*leggiero*), observing the dynamics. Remember to look ahead.

TRaK

K Is the key major or minor?

? Do you notice how the left hand imitates the right hand in bars 2 and 4?

Are there any changes of hand position?

There are G♯ accidentals throughout. Find any other accidentals.

In bars 9 and 10, both hands are playing the same notes but two octaves apart.

Practise moving from one position to another.

Do not forget to tap with both hands before you play. Remember the *staccato* crotchets.
Keep looking ahead in order to move this piece along (*Con moto*).

Follow the **TRaK**

? Do you notice how the intervals in the right hand contract and extend?

Can you look carefully at the suggested fingering, especially in the right hand?

The left hand part moves mostly in minim steps.

Note the extension of fingers in the last two bars (LH).

Relax, and play very quietly.

TRaK

K   Is this key major or minor?

?   Are there any tied notes?

If you are not sure about the key, look at the tonic in the last bar, and note the C♯s.

Apart from bars 5 to 8, all notes are marked *staccato*.

Even though there are several accidentals in this piece it is not as difficult as it first seems.
Use the rests in the last bars to get your fingers ready over the chords which follow.

T   On which beat of the bar does the piece begin?

R

K   Can you name the key?

?   What do you notice about the length of the two phrases?

Count carefully as you tap the rhythm.

The accidentals here might confuse you about the key. Check the tonic at the end of the piece.

Lift your wrist slightly to begin the second phrase.

Play this piece expressively, and try not to forget the *ritenuto* at the end.

Introducing the keys of A major and E minor

 ime, hythm and ey?

[?] How many ledger line notes are there in the left hand?

Find all the notes affected by the key signature.

At the end of the piece, give the tied interval of a fifth (LH) and tied interval of a fourth (RH) their full value.

....

Play the piece evenly, observing the *staccato* notes and slurs. Keep counting and look ahead.

[TRaK]

[?] What do you notice about the opening rhythm when you compare the two phrases?

What is a Gavotte?

How should you play the accent on the last chord?

Do not forget the G♯ in the key signature!

Notice how the melody is sometimes divided between the hands.

Main phrases begin on the third beat of the bar (one of the characteristics of a Gavotte).

Contrast the *staccato* notes with the slurred couplets.

....

Instead of counting 1–2–3–4, begin by counting 3–4–1–2 in order to achieve the style of the dance.

41

TRaK

K Which form of the minor scale do the C♯ and D♯ in bar 7 (LH) suggest?

? Can you name the chord in the last bar?

Can you make a note of the changes of finger on the repeated notes?

Another new key. The D♯ in bar 5 (RH) will help you to decide on the key.

This key is related to G major.

When a major third in the tonic chord concludes a piece in the minor, it is called a .... (see No. 24 for the answer).

Notice that the *staccato* notes are followed by *legato* notes (both hands).

Try sight-singing the melody first. Then play the piece through slowly (*Lento*).

42

T What is the time signature?

R Can you tap the rhythm of bars 1 and 2 (RH) a number of times before playing?

K What is the key?

? Can you study the fingering, especially in bars 9 and 10 (RH) and bar 12 (LH)?

The same rhythm appears in almost every bar in the right hand and in the last two bars of the left hand.

Do not forget the G♯ in the key signature.

See if any changes of hand position are needed. Look at bar 2 (LH).

Observe the dynamics especially in bar 5, and bars 11 to 12. Play rhythmically with a good strong tone.

T   On which beat does the tune begin?

R   Can you tap the rhythm?   Observe the crotchet rests.

K   Is the key major or minor? Play the tonic.   Find the F♯s and any accidentals.

?   Are bars 1–4 mainly smooth or mainly detached?   Contrast the second phrase with good *legato* playing.

Can you plan the fingering?   Look for any changes of hand position.

Do you know the meaning of *leggiero* and *dolce*?   The Italian term for the held minims (marked with the symbol '–') in bars 2 and 4 (RH) is *tenuto*.

TRaK

Explain **C** in the time signature.
Count as you tap the rhythm. Name the key.

?   Are there any tied notes?

Do you notice the changes of hand position at bars 2 and 3 (RH)?   Be prepared in advance!

Try to hear the melody in your head before you play. Remember all the sharps. Look ahead.

TRaK

K Can you name the key?

? Is there any imitation of the melody?

Can you study the fingering?

Look at the accidentals in bars 6 and 8 (RH) and the tonic note in the last bar.

This piece largely consists of short scale passages.

In bar 6, the 2nd finger must cross the thumb in both hands. You may like to try playing bars 5 and 6 before playing the whole piece through.

Let the music flow in a graceful manner.

T

R

K

? Are there any tied notes?

Do you notice the extension between the fingers in bars 1 and 2 (RH) and also in bar 4 (LH)?

There are ..... beats in a bar.

Tap this rhythm a few times:

1   2 *and* 3

Name the key. Find all the notes to be sharpened.

Notice also the change of hand position in bar 3 (LH).

Play lightly.

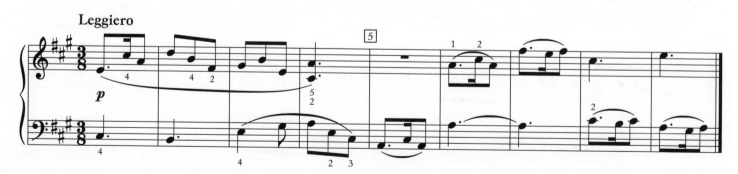

On your own now …

The following pieces do not have hints to help.

Remember … follow the TRaK , look ahead, keep counting and keep going!

52

Adagio

53

Allegro

54

Adagio

55

Adagio

56

Moderato

Allegro

mf leggiero

Moderato

Espressivo

cresc.

dim.

Sweetly

pp

pp

Allegretto

Moderato

Grazioso

77

78

79

84 **Ritmico**

85 **Maestoso**

86 **Agitato**

87 **With expression**

Leggiero

Largo

Tranquillo

Glossary of musical terms and symbols

Adagio	Slowly
Agitato	Agitated
Alla breve	[$\frac{2}{2}$ or ¢] two minim beats in a bar
Alla marcia	In the style of a march
Allegretto	Fairly quick, not as fast as *Allegro*
Allegro	(*lit.* cheerful) Quick, lively
Andante	Walking pace; moderate speed
Animato	Animated
Ben marcato	Very accented
Coda	(*lit.* a tail) A small passage added to the end of a piece
Con brio	With vigour
Con espressione	With expression
Con moto	With movement
Crescendo, cresc.	Gradually becoming louder
Diminuendo, dim.	Gradually becoming quieter
Dolce	Sweet
Espressivo	Expressive
*Forte (**mf**, **f**, **ff**)*	Loud (moderately loud, loud, very loud)
Giocoso	Playful, humorous
Grazioso	Graceful
Largo	Slow and stately
Legato	Smooth
Leggiero	Light
Lento	Slow
Maestoso	Majestic
Moderato	Moderate speed
*Piano (**mp**, **p**, **pp**)*	Quiet (fairly quiet, quiet, very quiet)
Più	More
Poco	Little
Rallentando, rall.	Gradually becoming slower
Ritenuto, rit.	Held back
Ritmico	Rhythmically
Scherzoso	Playfully
Tempo di marcia	In the time (and style) of a march
Tempo di menuetto	In the time (and style) of a minuet
Tempo di valse	In the time (and style) of a waltz
Tempo giusto	In strict time
Tenuto	Held (𝅗𝅥 ♩)
Tierce de Picardie	(*Fr.* for Picardy third)
	A *major* tonic chord which concludes a piece in a minor key
Tranquillo	Calm and tranquil
Vivace	Lively, quick
◁ (crescendo hairpin)	Gradually becoming louder
▷ (diminuendo hairpin)	Gradually becoming quieter
>	Accent